A Special Trip

by Sharon Franklin

HOUGHTON MIFFLIN   BOSTON

I was packed and ready to go for days. Finally, the big day arrived. Aunt Bess and I were leaving on a long trip. We would be gone for a whole month.

Aunt Bess said, "Jess, be sure and pack the right clothes for the weather." That wasn't easy! When you see the places we went to, you will understand my problem.

My aunt likes adventure. She wanted to take me on a trip from the equator to near the North Pole. Along the way, we had a chance to see how and why the climates were different.

Our first stop was Quito, Ecuador. It is only 22 miles from the equator. I figured it would be very hot and humid, so I wore shorts. When I mentioned my plan to my aunt, she just smiled. Now I know why.

South America

VENEZUELA

GUYANA
SURINAME
FRENCH GUIANA

COLOMBIA

Quito

Equator

ECUADOR

BRAZIL

PERU

BOLIVIA

PARAGUAY

CHILE

ARGENTINA

URUGUAY

3

Quito, Ecuador

Even though Quito is in a tropical climate, the city's elevation is at nearly 10,000 feet. That means it is really high above sea level. I soon found out that higher elevations mean cooler temperatures. It was a chilly 58°F in the daytime and dropped into the 40s at night. Both summer and winter temperatures average about 54°F.

Aunt Bess said some people think it's hotter on top of a mountain because you are closer to the Sun. Hot air does rise, she explained. However, air pressure goes down with elevation, so less air presses down on you. Because it is less dense, the air cools down. I also found out that low air pressure at high altitudes makes you short of breath.

Quito, Ecuador

Our next stop was Death Valley, California. I thought it would be a little warm. In fact, Death Valley once held the world record for the hottest temperature of 134F° in 1914! The day we arrived it was 121F°.

Death Valley holds another record. At 282 feet below sea level, it's the lowest place in the United States.

Death Valley is by definition a desert because it gets less than 10 inches of rain in a year. But Death Valley is a lot drier than that. It averages less than two inches of rain a year. It is the hottest, driest place in North America.

I asked my aunt what causes such dry weather. She said it was the rain shadow effect. This is how it works.

Many storms move onto California's west coast from the ocean. Much of the moisture stays in the clouds until they reach the Sierra Nevada Mountains. The clouds hit the mountains and are forced up. The mountains get rain or snow, but by the time the storm crosses the mountains, little moisture is left. Very little is left to fall on Death Valley.

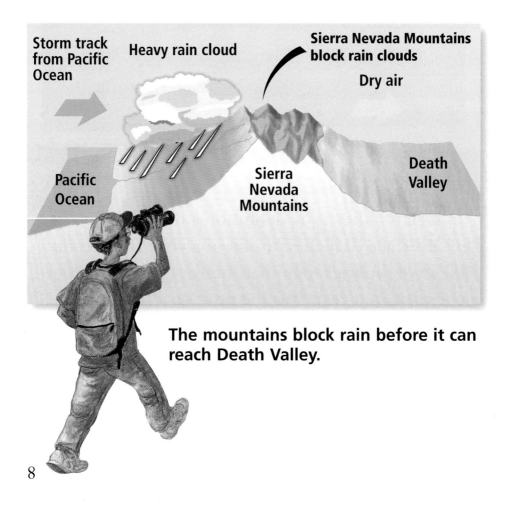

Storm track from Pacific Ocean

Heavy rain cloud

Sierra Nevada Mountains block rain clouds

Dry air

Pacific Ocean

Sierra Nevada Mountains

Death Valley

The mountains block rain before it can reach Death Valley.

When it does rain, there are often flash floods. We saw signs along the road, warning people to get to higher ground fast if it starts to rain! This is because the water doesn't soak into the dry ground. A hard rain can quickly send water and mud pouring across roads.

Olympic
National Park

Olympic
National Forest

WASHINGTON

Next, we headed for the Olympic National
Park in Washington state. I wore my sweatshirt but
soon put on my slicker. Between the rain and the
fog, it always dripped moisture. It was the perfect
environment for growing the most gigantic trees
I have ever seen. My aunt told me we were in a
temperate rain forest.

Olympic National Park, Wa.

It is the largest rain forest in the United States. A temperate rain forest has mild temperatures all year and gets more than 50 inches of rainfall a year.

The rain forest areas of Olympic National Park receive an average rainfall of more than 140 inches. Compare that to Death Valley!

A view of coastal mountains

In the Olympic National Forest, the moist Pacific Ocean air rises and is trapped by coastal mountains. The mountains protect the area. They keep it from getting too hot or too cold. They also trap the moisture, which falls as rain in the rain forest or snow in the mountains.

Our last stop was the Arctic Weather Station in Eureka, Canada. It is only 690 miles from the North Pole.

Although it was summer, it was 5°F the day we flew into this barren place. This rugged, very cold climate is actually a desert because it gets so little moisture. During the winter, it is always dark. It can reach a chilly -40°F.

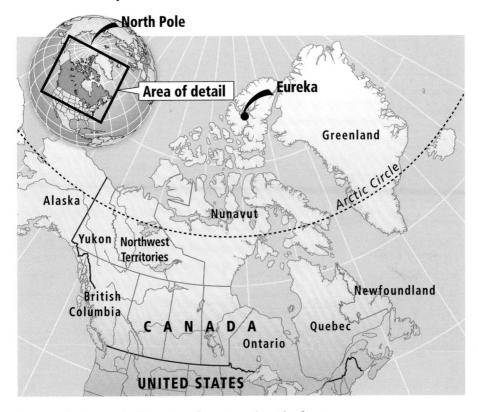

Part of Canada lies in the Arctic Circle.

I learned why the North Pole is so cold. Polar areas stay covered with snow and ice all year. Both poles are farthest from the equator and curved away from the sun. That means that the sun doesn't get high enough to melt the ice. Because ice is shiny, it reflects the sun's light and doesn't absorb the sun's heat the way land does.

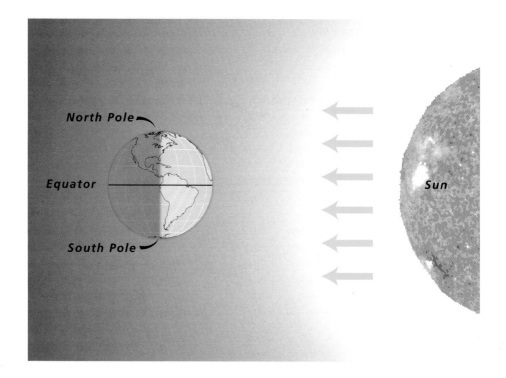

The North Pole is warmer than the South Pole.
Here's why. The North Pole is water with land around
it. The South Pole is land surrounded by ocean. The
Arctic's water is salt water, which stays warmer than
fresh water. Some heat comes up through the ice.
Its heat escapes into the air and warms it. Also, most
of the land of the South Pole is at high elevation.
I remember how that cools things down!

I had a great time on my trip. I also learned a lot. Sometimes we take the weather for granted. I will never do that again. And before I pack for another trip with my aunt, I will do some careful research!